Felt Turn

by Jason Plummer
illustrated by Doreen Gay-Kassel

Harcourt
SCHOOL PUBLISHERS

Requests for permission to make copies of any part of the work should be addressed to School Permissions and Copyrights, Harcourt, Inc., 6277 Sea Harbor Drive, Orlando, Florida 32887-6777. Fax: 407-345-2418.

HARCOURT and the Harcourt Logo are trademarks of Harcourt, Inc., registered in the United States of America and/or other jurisdictions.

Printed in China

ISBN 10: 0-15-350488-9
ISBN 13: 978-0-15-350488-4

Ordering Options
ISBN 10: 0-15-350333-5 (Grade 3 Below-Level Collection)
ISBN 13: 978-0-15-350333-7 (Grade 3 Below-Level Collection)
ISBN 10: 0-15-357474-7 (package of 5)
ISBN 13: 978-0-15-357474-0 (package of 5)

5 6 7 8 9 10 985 12 11 10 09

Felix stared at the shelf. There was a row of silver and gold cups. There was a row of shiny statues. Colored ribbons hung on the wall.

Felix sighed because none belonged to him. They all belonged to his older brother, Hector.

"Hector can do anything," said Felix.

"He's twelve and you're eight, so he's had more time," Mom said in a soothing voice.

"I'll never be able to win awards like he does," Felix replied.

"Yes, you will," said Mom, "but awards don't matter. Dad and I just want you to be happy."

Felix wasn't sure because Mom and Dad were always telling everybody about Hector and his awards.

"There must be something I can do that Hector can't," thought Felix. Then one day, Miss Parker talked to him after class.

"Felix, there's going to be a county spelling bee," said Miss Parker. "Since you won our class spelling bee, you will be going."

Felix raced home and looked at Hector's shelf of awards. There were no spelling prizes there.

"I'll be the spelling champ!" thought Felix. "Everyone will talk about me, not Hector."

He told his parents about the spelling bee that night. They were proud of him.

"That's great," said Hector.

Felix frowned because he wanted Hector to be *really* impressed. He hoped Hector would even be jealous.

Felix studied every night. He learned many new words, and he practiced with Mom and Dad. He spelled words they gave him and made sure that he spoke each letter clearly.

Finally, the day of the spelling bee came. Felix walked into the gym with his parents and Hector. The rows of chairs were filled with parents and kids waiting their turn.

The third graders went first. Felix breezed through the early rounds. All his words seemed easy, and that was very encouraging.

Finally, Felix and a boy named Will were the only ones left. Felix's word was "impressive."

"Impressive," said Felix. "I-M-P-R-E-S-I-V-E, impressive."

The host paused for a brief moment. Then he said, "I'm sorry, but that's incorrect." Will spelled the word correctly, and it was all over.

Will received a gold medal. Felix received a smaller silver one. He put it in his pocket and went outside.

Felix's parents praised him. He tried to smile. Then he told them that he had left something inside. The gym was empty now. Felix sat down and began to cry.

"Hey, what's going on?" someone said. It was Hector.

"This was my chance to do something you've never done, and I lost," Felix sobbed.

"You did do something I could never do," said Hector. "I could never spell on stage like that. How could you concentrate with all those people staring at you?"

"I don't know," said Felix.

"I'm scared of speaking in front of people," said Hector. "I thought you were impressive."

Felix laughed. "I actually liked it."

"That means you can do lots of things I can't," replied Hector. "When you do them, I'll be right there clapping for you. All right?"

Felix smiled. "All right."

"Come on," said Hector. "Mom made a big carrot cake for you. Don't tell her I told you!"

"I won't," said Felix. "You're a great big brother."

"I know," Hector said, chuckling. "Now let's go!"

Think Critically

1. Why does Felix enter the spelling bee?

2. How would you describe Felix?

3. Why does Felix wish that Hector would feel jealous of him?

4. Would you change the ending of this story? How?

5. Felix thinks that awards are very important. Do you agree with him? Why or why not?

 Social Studies

Geography Bee In geography bees, students answer questions about places. Make up and answer five questions about places near you. For example, what is your state capital?

School-Home Connection Think of an award you would like to give to someone in your family. Use paper or cardboard to make a medal. Give it to the person.